T0056203

Kurt Weill

Klopslied

(1925)

for Voice, Two Piccolos and Bassoon

On a traditional Berlin text: "Ick sitze da un' esse Klops"
according to the text of the Kurt Weill Edition (Ser. II, Vol. 1)
edited by Wolfgang Rathert and Jürgen Selk

EAMC 849

Preface

Chamber music comprises only a relatively small portion of Weill's œuvre; it is represented by the Streichquartett in h-Moll (String Quartet in B minor), the I. Streichquartett op. 8 (String Quartet No. 1, op. 8), the Sonate für Violoncello und Klavier (Sonata for Violoncello and Piano), the vocal-instrumental song cycle *Frauentanz* op. 10, and the vocal-instrumental miniature *Ick sitze da – un esse Klops* (*I sit here – eating meatballs*). These works were published in 2004 in a critical edition edited by Wolfgang Rathert and Jürgen Selk, as part of the Kurt Weill Edition (Series II, Volume 1). The present performing edition of the *Meatball Song* derives from the text of the critical edition.

Except for the *Meatball Song*, composed ca. 1925–26, Weill wrote his remaining chamber music between 1918 and 1923. It reflects both Weill's development as a young composer as well as the external circumstances which influenced his progress, beginning with his studies at the *Königlich Akademische Hochschule für Musik* in Berlin under Engelbert Humperdinck (1918–19), his brief tenure as conductor in Lüdenscheid (1919–20), and his studies in Ferruccio Busoni's masterclass, beginning in 1921.

From the String Quartet in B minor (1918–19), completed under Humperdinck's tutelage, to the Sonata for Violoncello and Piano (1919–20), Weill's style undergoes a remarkable transformation. The String Quartet in B minor shows a clear orientation toward classical models; it is characterized by a late-romantic idiom that points toward the influence of Richard Strauss, Hans Pfitzner, and Max Reger (as shown, for example, in the expansive fugal finale of the last movement). Weill's Sonata for Violoncello and Piano, on the other hand, signals a clear departure from this idiom; its expanded and unconventional harmonic vocabulary suggests instead the influence of Debussy.

A clear dividing line separates these first two works of Weill's chamber music from his next two contributions, the String Quartet No. 1, op. 8 and the song cycle *Frauentanz* op. 10. One important difference is immediately apparent in the manuscripts: Weill's notation on the whole has become clearer and more precise. Universal Edition had accepted these two works for publication, and one suspects that for this reason, Weill was especially careful in his notation, knowing that his manuscripts would serve as engraver's models. But stylistically as well these two works differ significantly from his String Quartet in B minor and his Sonata for Violoncello and Piano; they point toward Ferruccio Busoni, whose vision of a "new classicality" exerted a considerable influence on Weill.

Among Weill's chamber works, *Ick sitze da – un esse Klops* is a unique case. One might argue that classification as a *Lied* would be more appropriate. The instrumentation, for two piccolos, bassoon, and voice, is reminiscent of *Frauentanz*. Weill wrote the piece on the occasion of the twenty-fifth anniversary (1926) of Universal Edition; he dedicated it to the director of U. E., Emil Hertzka. Weill's autograph was included in a presentation volume together with musical contributions by other composers under contract at Universal Edition. After Hertzka's death, the volume was broken up again and the autographs were sold off individually. Currently, Weill's autograph resides at the Pierpont Morgan Library in New York City. The *Meatball Song* received its first performance on 14 December 1927 on the occasion of Thea and Hans Heinz Stuckenschmidt's wedding in Prague.

The text of the *Meatball Song* is an anonymous poem that was apparently quite popular in Berlin in the 1920s. The poem appears in two publications from 1925; Weill may have taken the poem from either of these two publications (see the critical edition).

As the two-page autograph is the only source for *Ick sitze da – un esse Klops*, this edition is derived solely from it. Given its intended purpose as a dedicatory composition, Weill's notation is clean and poses no significant editorial challenges. Up until now, the *Meatball Song* has been published only in an arrangement for voice and piano by Lys Symonette (published in 1982 in *The Unknown Weill* by European American Music). With the present edition, *Ick sitze da – un esse Klops* is now available for the first time in its original version.

Jürgen Selk
New York City, July 2005

Vorwort

Im Gesamtwerk Kurt Weills nimmt Kammermusik einen verhältnismäßig kleinen Teil ein; der Gesamtbestand umfaßt das *Streichquartett in h-Moll*, das *I. Streichquartett op. 8*, die *Sonate für Violoncello und Klavier*, den vokal-instrumentalen Liederzyklus *Frauentanz op. 10* sowie die vokal-instrumentale Miniatur *Ick sitze da – un esse Klops*. Diese Werke wurden im Jahre 2004 in einer kritischen Edition, herausgegeben von Wolfgang Rathert und Jürgen Selk, als Teil der Kurt Weill Edition veröffentlicht (Serie II, Band 1). Die hier vorliegende praktische Ausgabe des *Klopslieds* beruht auf dem Text der kritischen Edition.

Mit Ausnahme des *Klopslieds*, das Weill etwa 1925–26 komponierte, stammt Weills Kammermusik aus den Jahren 1918–23. In ihr sind sowohl Weills Entwicklung als junger Komponist reflektiert als auch die äußeren Umstände, die seinen Werdegang beeinflußten, beginnend mit seinem Studium an der Königlich Akademischen Hochschule für Musik in Berlin unter Engelbert Humperdinck (1918–19), seiner vorübergehenden Tätigkeit als Kapellmeister in Lüdenscheid (1919–20) und schließlich seinem Studium in Ferruccio Busonis Meisterklasse, beginnend im Jahre 1921.

Schon zwischen dem *Streichquartett in h-Moll* (1918–19), dessen Fertigstellung im Rahmen von Humperdincks Unterricht erfolgte, und der *Sonate für Violoncello und Klavier* (1919–20) zeigt sich eine bemerkenswerte stilistische Entwicklung. Während sich das *Streichquartett in h-Moll* noch eindeutig an klassischen Vorbildern orientiert und in einer spätromantischen Sprache verfaßt ist, die den Einfluß von Richard Strauss, Hans Pfitzner und Max Reger erkennen läßt – wie zum Beispiel in dem ausgedehnten Fugenfinale des letzten Satzes – manifestiert sich in der *Sonate für Violoncello und Klavier* ein Duktus, der mit der Sprache des *Streichquartetts in h-Moll* nur noch wenig gemeinsam hat, das harmonische Vokabular rigoros – und mitunter unkonventionell – erweitert und stilistisch eher einen Einfluß Debussys nahelegt.

Ein klare Demarkationslinie trennt diese ersten beiden kammermusikalischen Werke Weills von den nächsten beiden, dem *I. Streichquartett op. 8* und seinem Liederzyklus *Frauentanz op. 10*. Dies macht sich sofort augenfällig bemerkbar, indem Weills autographe Notation insgesamt bedeutend klarer und unmißverständlicher wird, was auch darauf zurückzuführen ist, daß diese beiden Werke von der Universal Edition angenommen und veröffentlicht wurden und Weill sich deshalb bemühte, im Hinblick auf die Verwendung dieser Partituren als Stichvorlagen, seine Intentionen deutlicher zu fixieren. Aber auch stilistisch unterscheiden sich diese beiden Werke merklich vom *Streichquartett in h-Moll* sowie der *Sonate für Violoncello und Klavier*: sie weisen deutlich auf den Einfluß Ferruccio Busonis hin, dessen Idee einer „jungen Klassizität" einen beträchtlichen Eindruck auf Weill ausübte.

In der Kammermusik Weills stellt *Ick sitze da – un esse Klops* ein Unikum dar. Man könnte darüber diskutieren, ob diese Miniatur passender als „Lied" zu klassifizieren sei. Die Instrumentierung des Stückes, für zwei Pikkoloflöten, Fagott und Stimme erinnert an *Frauentanz*. Das Stück ist eine Gelegenheitskomposition, die Weill etwa 1925–26 aus Anlaß des fünfundzwanzigjährigen Jubiläums (1926) der Universal Edition schrieb und dem Verleger Emil Hertzka widmete. Weills Autograph wurde in einen Geschenkband integriert, zusammen mit musikalischen Beiträgen anderer Komponisten bei der Universal Edition. Nach Hertzkas Tod wurde dieser Band aufgetrennt und die einzelnen Autographe wurden verkauft. Zur Zeit befindet sich Weills Autograph in der Pierpont Morgan Library in New York. Die erste Aufführung des *Klopslieds* erfolgte am 14. Dezember 1927 bei der Hochzeit von Thea und Hans Heinz Stuckenschmidt in Prag.

Der Text des *Klopslieds* ist ein anonymes Gedicht, das im Berlin der zwanziger Jahre einigermaßen verbreitet war; bislang sind zwei Veröffentlichungen aus dem Jahre 1925 bekannt, in denen das Gedicht im Druck erschien. Es ist denkbar, daß Weill den Text einer dieser Veröffentlichungen entnahm (siehe dazu die Kritische Edition).

Die Quellenlage des *Klopslieds* ist denkbar einfach: es existiert lediglich das zweiseitige Autograph. Diese Ausgabe lehnt sich daher ausschließlich an diese Quelle an, die als sauber notierte Widmungskomposition keine besonderen editorischen Hürden aufweist. Bislang lag das *Klopslied* nur in einer von Lys Symonette eingerichteten Bearbeitung für Stimme und Klavier im Druck vor (in *The Unknown Weill*, erschienen 1982 bei European American Music Corporation). Mit der vorliegenden Ausgabe des *Klopslieds* ist diese Miniatur in seiner Originalfassung nun zum ersten Mal allgemein zugänglich.

Jürgen Selk
New York City, Juli 2005

Ick sitze da–un esse Klops

Kurt Weill
(1900-1950)

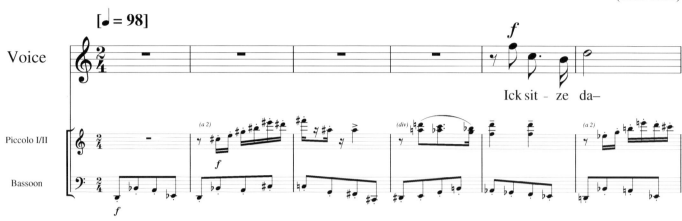

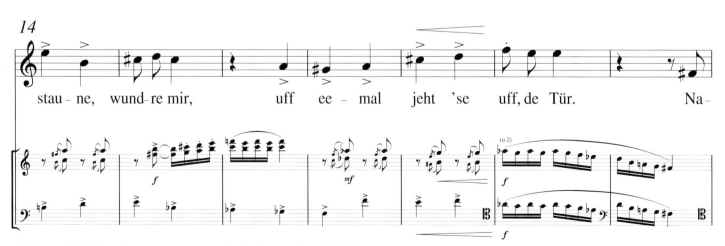

Ick sitze da–un esse Klops

Bassoon

Kurt Weill
(1900-1950)

Ick sitze da–un esse Klops

Kurt Weill
(1900-1950)

EAMC 849

Printed in U.S.A.

Ick sitze da–un esse Klops

Kurt Weill
(1900-1950)

Piccolo II

-nu, denk ick, ick denk na - nu, jetzt is 'se uff, erscht war 'se zu-

molto string.

Ick je - he raus un blik - ke un wer steht drau - -

rit. **Presto**

- ssen?: Ik-ke Ik-ke Ik-ke.

Dies wünscht Ihnen, verehrter Herr Direktor Hertzka,

Ihr ergebener Kurt Weill.